I'm A Christian Now!

Todd Capps   Sherry Shaw

OLDER KIDS

R E V I S E D

LifeWay Press®
Nashville, TN 37234

ISBN: 9781415867419
Item #005191566
This book is a resource in the
category of the Christian Growth Study Plan.
Course
DEWEY: J248.82
SUBHD: CHILDREN—RELIGIOUS LIFE \ DISCIPLESHIP \ REGENERATION (CHRISTIANITY)

Printed in the United States of America

Childhood Ministry Publishing
LifeWay Church Resources
One LifeWay Plaza
Nashville, Tennessee 37234-0172

We believe the Bible has God for its author; salvation for its end;
and truth, without any mixture of error, for its matter
and that all Scripture is totally true and trustworthy.
The 2000 statement of *The Baptist Faith and Message* is our doctrinal guideline.

You're a Christian now!

What an exciting time in your life! This book will help you understand what it means to be a Christian. Deciding to become a Christian is a once-in-a-lifetime decision. You cannot do anything that will stop you from being a Christian. You can never do anything that will cause God to stop loving you! Being a Christian means you have a relationship with God. What Jesus did makes a relationship with God possible.

Learning how to be a better Christian is something you do each day. As you grow, you learn new things. As a Christian, you will be learning new things about God, Jesus, the Bible, your church, and yourself! This book will help you get started.

When you finish this book, you will not have all the answers. You should have a better idea of how to find answers about being a Christian. This book will also help you learn how to tell others about Jesus and how He makes a difference in your life.

How to use this book:

Use this book every day. Try not to skip a day or do more than one day at a time. This is new information for you, and you need time to understand it. Find a quiet place where you won't be tempted to watch TV or do other things. There will be some days that do not have as much to do as other days. The important thing to remember is to work in your book *every* day!

To help you set aside some time every day, fill in the blanks:

I will work in my workbook every day at

[write in a time]

I will work in my workbook in

[write in a place]

You can write this time and place information on a separate sheet of paper. Put this sheet where you will see it often. Tape it on your bathroom mirror or to your bedroom door. Make sure you put it in a place where you will see it every day.

Things to have when you use this book:
3-by-5-inch cards
your Bible
a pen or pencil
an inexpensive notebook
a Memory Box
(See pages 24-25.)

Christian
[KRISS chuhn]
is the name given to a person
who has asked Jesus to be
his Lord and Savior.

When you became a Christian, you made the most important decision of your life. Today you will begin to learn what it means to be a Christian!

When you became a Christian, you asked Jesus to be your Lord and Savior. Right now, you probably do not understand what that means. This book will help you begin your life as a Christian.

Fast Fact

Read Acts 11:26 to find out where Jesus' followers were first called Christians. Followers of Jesus were first called Christians in a place called _____. Using your secret "decoder" magnifying glass (red cellophane), look at the word in the circle to see if you got the right answer:

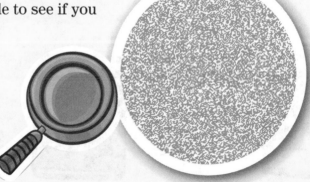

Jesus provided the way for all people to become Christians. Find John 3:16 in your Bible. Does this verse sound familiar to you? That's because it's your memory verse for the week and you hear it a lot in church and Sunday School. Because this verse is important, you need to memorize it.

While you have your Bible open, write out John 3:16 on a 3-by-5-inch card. Keep this card in a place where you will see it often. You can keep it in your notebook, or you could tape it to your bathroom mirror. If you happen to lose it, make another one! (If you can't write all of it on the front of the card, keep writing on the back.)

On another card, write *I became a Christian* on-_____ (fill in the month, day, and year when you became a Christian). Decorate the card with stickers, drawings, or color it. Make it a special memory keepsake. When you are finished, place it in your Memory Box.

i bEcaME a CHRiStiaN oN Nov. 30. 2008

Baptism

Memory Box

Thank God for loving you so much that He sent Jesus to save you. Tell God that you like being called a Christian. Ask Him to help you learn more about Jesus.

Sin
means any actions, attitudes, words, or thoughts that do not please God.

With the definition of sin in mind, write some things on the lines below that you think are sins. (For example, cheating on a test or lying to your parents is sin. Try to think of other sins for your list.)

Read John 1:29 and see what Jesus does about sin. There are seven words. The first letter of each word is given to you.

Jesus t_____

a_____

t_____ s_____ o____ t_____

w_____.

Decode it! Check your answers using your decoder on the circle.

Reread the definition for *sin* on page 6. When you do something that is wrong, it is a sin. It is also a sin if you choose not to do something that is right. Can you think of an example of doing nothing that would be a sin? If you need a example, read on!

Manny met Drew the day his family moved into the house next door. Because they had played together during the weekend, Drew decided to ask if he could join Manny and his friends during recess at school. Jason, one of Manny's friends, began to tease Drew and say mean things that hurt Drew's feelings. Manny just stood there and said nothing.

Even though Manny did not do anything to Drew, his actions were wrong. The fact that he did nothing to help Drew was not pleasing to God.

In the space below, write something that you have done and think is a sin.

I have…

_____

_____

_____

Ask God to forgive you for that sin. Ask God to help you not to do that sin anymore.

Ask your parents if one of them has a bulletin or another item from the day you were baptized for your Memory Box. If you haven't been baptized yet, make yourself a note to remember to save something for your Memory Box from that day.

Repent *[REE pent]*
means to turn from disobeying God to obeying Him. It means to be sorry for the sin in your life and to live the way God wants you to live.

Learn it!

Repenting is the first step in becoming a Christian. Repenting means that you understand you need to ask God for forgiveness and need to ask Him for help to live your life. The Holy Spirit is God's Spirit who helps you to admit you are a sinner and to repent.

Maybe this example can help you understand what *repent* means. Imagine you are going on a trip with your parents. Your mom tells your dad that he is going the wrong way. What should your dad do? Should he keep going in the same direction or should he turn around and go in the opposite direction? He should turn around and go the opposite direction.

That's a simple definition of what repent means. It means you know that what you are doing is wrong and you choose not to do that action anymore. When you realize you have done something wrong, you should pray and ask God to forgive you. You should also ask God to help you not to do that action again. That's what repenting is!

Repentance

Do it!

Let's see if you've gotten the basic idea of the meaning of "repent." Find a family member and explain what **repent** means and then see if you can demonstrate it for her.

Find it!

For Christians, *repent* means to turn away from living life as you choose and to live the way that God wants you to live. Jesus said that He came to earth to ask sinners to repent and turn to God. To read this for yourself, look up Luke 5:32 in your Bible.

Look at the picture below. How could Joni show repentance to Maria? Fill in the speech bubbles with what each girl should say to the other. What else should take place?

Use your decoder on the box on the right. Are your answers similar?

Save
means to be rescued, brought to safety, or delivered from the judgment of sin.

Learn it!

Mark through the statements below that do not show what the word *save* means. You should mark through three statements. One statement should be left. Write that one statement in the bubble on the bottom of the next page. *Save* does not mean:

Deleting a file on your computer's hard drive.

Rescuing a person from death or anything that might hurt or destroy.

Throwing away something that you might want to use later.

Not putting your bicycle in the garage to keep it from getting wet or damaged.

In your own words, what does *save* mean?

_____

_____

To help you understand the meaning of *save*, think about what a firefighter does. You have probably seen a firefighter in person or on TV. What does a firefighter do?

_____

_____

Firefighters and other emergency rescue workers are very important, especially if you are in trouble! Sometimes firefighters risk their own lives in order to save someone else. Firefighters save people from physical danger.

Romans 3:23 says that every person has sinned. When you became a Christian, Jesus saved you from the punishment for sin. Romans 6:23 tells what the punishment for sin is. This verse says that the punishment for sin is death. Romans 6:23 also says that God gives you eternal life through Jesus. Jesus saved you from the judgment of sin. Because Jesus has saved you, you have been rescued from death.

This does not mean that you will never die a physical death. It means that you will live forever with Jesus. Every person will die someday. Because Jesus has saved you, you will live forever with Him in heaven after you die. The great thing about being a Christian is that you can have a relationship with Jesus now. He loves you and saved you.

Do you remember your memory verse for the week? It is John 3:16. This verse says that Jesus loves you so much that He died so that you could be with God forever. If you haven't memorized this verse yet, try to memorize it now.

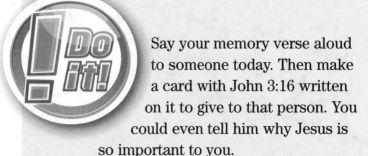

Say your memory verse aloud to someone today. Then make a card with John 3:16 written on it to give to that person. You could even tell him why Jesus is so important to you.

You shared John 3:16 with a friend, now share it with someone in your family. This time, put your name in the verse in place of "the world" when you say it. Does that make you feel special? It should! Tell someone in your family what the verse means and show her how her name fits in the verse.

Write John 3:16 with your name in it. How do you feel when you read the verse written with your name added to it?

_____

_____

_____

_____

_____

_____

Thank God for giving Jesus to save you from your sin. Ask Him to help you tell someone about Jesus this week. Write his or her name in the blank.

Testimony
[TES tuh mow nee]
means telling about
your experience.

Holy Spirit
is the Spirit of God who helps
people understand and accept
God's plan of salvation.

FIND IT!

Your testimony is just that—*your* testimony. No one else has a story like yours. The way the Holy Spirit helped you know that you needed to become a Christian is your testimony. When you tell others how you became a Christian, you are sharing your testimony!

Let's see what the Bible says about testimonies. Look up 2 Thessalonians 1:10. In this letter to the Christians in Thessalonica *[THESS uh loh NIGH kuh]*, Paul talked about others' believing the testimony of Paul, Silas, and Timothy. In other words, people there believed in Jesus because of the statements made by Paul, Silas, and Timothy. Stop and think: do you know someone who hasn't heard about Jesus? Write that person's name in the space below.

PRAY IT!

Thank God that you can tell others about Jesus. Ask God to help you tell the person you listed earlier about Jesus.

Don't Forget Your ABCs

If you need help telling someone about Jesus, remember to review your ABCs.

A: Admit to God that you are a sinner.

B: Believe that Jesus is God's only Son.

C: Confess your faith in Jesus as your Savior and Lord.

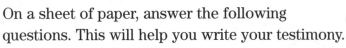 

On a sheet of paper, answer the following questions. This will help you write your testimony.

How would you help someone to become a Christian?

When did you first start thinking about becoming a Christian?

Why did you think that you needed to become a Christian?

Explain what happened when you became a Christian.

How is your life different since you became a Christian?

How would you help someone to become a Christian?

After you finish writing this, you should share it with someone. Why don't you share it with the person whose name you listed in "Find It!" section? You did it! You gave your testimony about Jesus!

 Find and read Luke 6:46.

 Find and read Luke 2:52.

 Jesus is Lord when you do what He has told you to do.

 In what three ways did Jesus grow? Write your answer here.

 Ask God to help you do what Jesus wants you to do.

 Ask God to help you grow in the ways that Jesus grew.

Learn it!

An **ordinance** is a special event of the church.

Baptism means to obey God by being put under water to show that you have become a Christian.

The **Lord's Supper** is a special time to help Christians remember Jesus' death.

Baptism and the Lord's Supper are ordinances of the church. An ordinance is a law or command given by Jesus that His followers are to obey. The first churches wanted to remember the life of Jesus and what He had done for them. They used two of Jesus' examples to remember His death, burial, and resurrection: baptism and the Lord's Supper.

As a Christian, you are a follower of Jesus and should participate with your church in the ordinances of baptism and the Lord's Supper.

Baptism

Baptism shows that a person has turned away from the way he used to live, has asked Jesus into his life, and wants to follow Jesus every day. Becoming a Christian comes first—baptism does not make a person a Christian. The act of baptism is a reminder of Jesus' death, burial, and resurrection. When a person is baptized, he is immersed in water. (*Immersed* means to be put under water completely.)

The Lord's Supper

To help His disciples remember Him, Jesus shared a special meal with them. At the meal He used bread and wine to show them what would happen to His body. Today the church continues to share the Lord's Supper as a way of remembering Jesus' death.

The Lord's Supper

This week's memory verse can help you remember how Jesus feels when you follow His commands. Find John 15:14 in your Bible and print it on a 3-by-5-inch card. Place the card in a location you will see each day to help you learn the verse this week.

Answer the following questions:

How do you think it makes your *parents* feel when you obey them?

_____

_____

How do you think it makes *Jesus* feel when you obey Him?

_____

How does it make *you* feel when you obey Jesus?

_____

How does it make *you* feel when you do not obey Jesus?

_____

_____

This week you will learn more about Jesus' baptism and the last meal He shared with His disciples.

Thank God for sending Jesus. Ask Him to help you learn to obey Him in everything He tells you to do.

Open your Bible to Matthew 3:13-17 and read about Jesus' baptism. Create a picture in the space below of what you think is taking place in the story.

Do you remember the first time you saw someone being baptized?

_____

What did you think was happening to that person?

_____

How do you think the water felt?

_____

Thank Jesus for the example He gave by being baptized. Ask Him to help you to be an example to others. Ask Jesus to help you continue to obey Him each day.

Learn it!

Who baptized Jesus? _____
(You can check your answer by using your decoder on the circle.)

Imagine you were John. How would you have felt if Jesus came to you and asked you to baptize Him? John felt that he needed to be baptized *by* Jesus instead of being the one to baptize Jesus. Jesus said that John needed to baptize Him to help Him fulfill what God had sent Him to do. Jesus set an example for Christians to follow through His baptism.

The first churches baptized because of the example Jesus had given them and also because He commanded them to do so. This week's memory verse helps you know what happens when you obey Jesus. Do you remember the memory verse? (If you don't, review your card from yesterday.) It says to obey what Jesus commanded.

What happened when Jesus came out of the water? (Read Matthew 3:16-17.)
How did God respond to Jesus?

_____

How did your family respond when you became a Christian?

_____

Who was the first person you told when you became a Christian?

_____

Do it!

Find someone in your family, church, school, or neighborhood and ask them the following questions. If you have already been baptized, you can compare your answers with the answers of those you ask.

How old were you when you became a Christian? _____

When you were baptized, how did you feel?

_____

What do you remember about the day you were baptized?

_____

17

Week 2
Day THREE

Think about the last few days. What are some decisions you have had to make? Did you decide

- which shoes should you wear?
- whether or not to do your homework?
- what you wanted to eat for an afternoon snack?

How many of the decisions you made really mattered? Does it really matter which pair of shoes you wore last Tuesday? Not at all! Some decisions are much more important. The decision you made to become a Christian is the most important decision you will ever make!

FiND iT!

Today you will read about a man who decided to follow Jesus. His decision changed his life and the lives of everyone in his family. Read Acts 16:25-34.

18

Learn it!

Do it!

Where were Paul and Silas? Because of their decision to follow Jesus and tell others about Him, they were arrested and put in jail. Even while they were in prison, they were able to tell others about Jesus. Look at verse 31.
What did Paul and Silas say people had to do to be saved?

_____

_____

The jailer confessed his belief in Jesus and was saved. As a result, he and his whole family became Christians. After confessing that he believed in Jesus, the jailer was baptized. Did you notice the order? He became a Christian and then he was baptized.
The decision to ask Jesus into his life was a very important one. Being baptized did not make the jailer a Christian, but it showed others that he had become a Christian.

Have you and your family discussed when you will be baptized? If not, talk with your family and pastor about setting a date. Write the date you plan to be baptized here:

_____

(If you have already been baptized, write the date you were baptized.)

Do you have questions about being baptized? If you do, make a list of questions you want to ask your pastor when you meet with him to talk about your baptism.

Pray it!

Thank God for the people in your life who helped you know how to become a Christian. Ask God to help you tell others how much He loves them.

19

Week 2 Day FOUR

When a person dies, family members remember that person in different ways. Think about a special person in your family who is no longer living. It could be a grandmother, grandfather, aunt, or uncle. How does your family remember this person? Some families look through pictures and share stories they remember about the person. Other families read journals or letters the person wrote.

Fast Fact

In 1869, Dr. Thomas Bramwell Welch, a doctor and dentist, successfully pasteurized Concord grape juice to use at his church in Vineland, New Jersey.

Learn it!

Jesus knew that His life on earth would soon come to an end. It was time for Him to complete what God had sent Him to do. Read Luke 22:14-22. In the last meal before He died, Jesus used two common items to help His disciples remember Him. What were the two items Jesus used? Place your decoder over the circle to discover the answer.

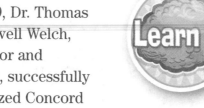

In Jesus' time, bread was a common food served at most meals. Jesus knew the disciples would see the bread often and remember Him. Jesus took the bread, thanked God for it, broke it, and gave it to His disciples to eat. He told them that the bread represented His body, which would be broken for them. The next day, Jesus' body would be broken, or hurt, as He was nailed to the cross.

Like the bread, Jesus took the cup, thanked God for it, and told the disciples to drink it. He said the drink would remind them of His blood that would be poured out for them. When Jesus was nailed to the cross, His body bled, pouring out His blood.

Do you know why Jesus told the disciples to eat the bread and drink from the cup? He told them to do so to remember Him (Look at verse 19.). Every time your church observes the Lord's Supper, they are remembering the death of Jesus. They are remembering how Jesus' body was broken and how His blood was poured out when He was crucified on the cross.

When your church shares in the Lord's Supper, it is a special time of remembering Jesus' death. How does the death of Jesus make you feel?

Write a thank-you letter to Jesus for dying on the cross for you.

Thank Jesus for dying for you. Ask Him to help you live your life the way He would have you do. Tell Jesus how much you love Him!

21

Week 2 Day FIVE

Read 1 Corinthians 11:27-34. Answer each of the statements with *T* for true or *F* for false. After you have answered all of them, use your decoder on page 23 to check your answers.

_____ If I have said something wrong about a person, I should ask that person to forgive me before I participate in the Lord's Supper.

_____ I should ask God to forgive all my sins before I participate in the Lord's Supper.

_____ I should not participate in the Lord's Supper to meet my hunger needs.

_____ I should remember that the reason I am participating in the Lord's Supper is to remember the death of Jesus.

_____ I should be a Christian before I participate in the Lord's Supper.

_____ I should pray and thank God for the gift of Jesus He has given me.

How should you behave during the Lord's Supper?

_____

Review

This week you have learned about two ordinances of the church. What are the two ordinances?

1 [   ]

Why does your church observe these ordinances?

2 [   ]

The manner in which you participate in the Lord's Supper is important. The Lord's Supper is not a feast. It is to help you remember Jesus' death.

Do you remember John 15:14? If not, review the verse you wrote on a card at the beginning of the week. Jesus commanded the disciples to remember Him through the Lord's Supper. You are following John 15:14 when you participate in the Lord's Supper.

The first time you take part in the Lord's Supper, fill in the information below:

The first time I took part in the Lord's Supper was _____.

My pastor was _____.

I felt _____.

My favorite part was _____

_____.

22

Do you have questions about the Lord's Supper? If you do, list them here and ask your parents or your pastor to help you find answers to your questions.

Do you need to ask God to forgive you for something wrong you have done? Ask Him to forgive you. He will because He loves you!

Week 2 Day SIX

Find and read Acts 2:38 and 41.

What was Peter's message? How did the people respond?

Ask God to help you tell others about your baptism. If you have not been baptized yet, ask God to help you tell someone why you plan to be baptized and invite that person to attend.

Week 2 Day SEVEN

Find and read 1 Corinthians 11:26.

What does this verse say you are doing when you take the Lord's Supper?

Pray that God will give you a chance to tell someone about Jesus this week.

Memory Box

When you made the decision to become a Christian, it was a special time. When your pastor talked to you and your parents about your decision, he probably spoke to you about baptism and the Lord's Supper. The next time your church celebrates the Lord's Supper will be a special time for you. It'll be your first Lord's Supper. To help you remember these special times, you can place things in a special Memory Box to help you remember these experiences.

To make a Memory Box, you will need a box. A shoe box or school box should be large enough. Decorate your box any way you choose. You can cover it with colored paper, stickers, your own drawings, or anything else you want.

As you work in this guide, you will see suggestions of things to gather or prepare so you can place them in your Memory Box. On the next page are some other suggestions of things you may want to remember to gather or do for your Memory Box.

- your first Lord's Supper plastic cup

- the handkerchief the pastor uses to cover your nose and mouth when you are baptized

- your baptism certificate

- a letter from your pastor or Sunday School teacher that tells others about you

- a picture of you the day you told the church about your decision

- a video or photo of your baptism

- a video or CD recording of you talking about your decision to become a Christian

- the completed "All About Me" information on page 47

These are just a few suggestions. This is your Memory Box! Make it a special place for you to keep things to remind you of your first days as a new Christian. As you work though this book, you will think of other things to add to your Memory Box.

Church Membership

Name
Carla G
Date of Birth
5.11.02
Parents

DVD of being baptized

Dear Class,

This morning our friend Eddie was baptized.

Church is a group of baptized believers in Jesus who have chosen to do the work of God together. Anyone can *attend* a church, but you cannot be a member of the church unless you have been baptized.

> **Church is a group of baptized believers.**

Learn it!

This week you will be learning about the church—what it is and what you can do as a part of the church.

When Jesus was young, He and His family attended the synagogue. A synagogue was made up of a group of Jewish people who gathered to hear someone read and explain the Old Testament books of the law and the prophets. They also would have prayer. Every week they worshiped God with others who believed in God.

Aren't you glad there is a place you can go to meet with other people who believe in Jesus? Today churches gather to be able to learn more about God, Jesus, and the Bible. Every church is different. Even church buildings are different. Some churches meet in big buildings that have steeples and crosses. Other churches meet in school buildings. In Africa, some churches meet outside or under shelters that have grass roofs.

Look up Psalm 122:1 in your Bible. This is your memory verse for this week. Remember, the Book of Psalms is found in the Old Testament. Write the verse on a 3-by-5-inch card. Place the card where you can read it often. Begin memorizing the verse today. One way to memorize is to write it several times on a sheet of paper.

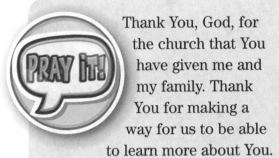

Thank You, God, for the church that You have given me and my family. Thank You for making a way for us to be able to learn more about You.

Fast Fact

In some countries, people come together to worship under a tree or in a building that looks like a shack. It doesn't matter where people meet to worship. Jesus said that where two or more people gather in His name, He is with them. (See Matthew 18:20.)

Read the questions and fill in your answers in the spaces provided.

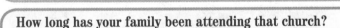

Which church do you attend?

Why do you attend that church?

How long has your family been attending that church?

Pastor
Who is the pastor of your church?

_____

Worship Leader
Who leads the music in your church?

_____

Sunday School Teacher
Who are your Sunday School teachers?

_____

_____

Janitor
Who takes care of your church building to make sure that it is clean and ready for you and other children each week?

_____

Use your decoder to find some clues for jobs you can do at church.

What are the "jobs" that people do at church? Do you think you can guess? In the space below, draw some items that you think people use at church. For example, you could draw a picture of a Bible or a broom.

Learn it!

What kind of jobs do you think you can do? Can you name them here?

_____

_____

_____

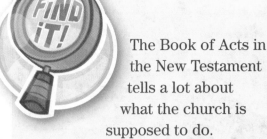

The Book of Acts in the New Testament tells a lot about what the church is supposed to do.

In Acts 2:42, four specific things are mentioned that the church should be doing. List the four things here:

1. _____

2. _____

3. _____

4. _____

See if you can fit these words into the crossword puzzle. If you want to check your answers, use your decoder over the red circle below.

Does your church do these things? If your church is to continue to reach more people and tell them about Jesus, it must do these four things.

Thank God for your church and for the church leaders. Ask Him to help you know what things you can to do to help others in your church.

Look at the things you listed. On a 3-by-5-inch card, write three things- you can do to help at your church.- Tell someone at your church that you would like to help do these things. Then put your list in your Memory Box.

Day THREE

What can your church do to help others?

Do you remember the song "I Can Be a Helper"? This song reminds you that Christians can be helpers anywhere they go. What are some ways that your church can be a helper to people who live in the community?

Using some of the things on your list, put the ways your church can be a helper to a tune and create a new song. Write your new song here:

Look at the Bible passage you read yesterday, Acts 2:42. Do you remember the four things the church was doing in this verse? List them here.

Grade

1. - _____ _____

2. - _____ _____

3. - _____ _____

4. - _____ _____

If your church were graded in these four areas, what grade would your church get? On the list you just made, give your church a grade in each of the four areas listed. You may wish to talk to your parents about your church. There is always room for improvement.

Where does your church need to improve most?

_____

In which area does your church get the highest grade?

_____

Write a note to your pastor. Tell him that you think your church is doing a great job following what Acts 2:42 says the church should be doing. Give the note to your pastor the next time you see him at church.

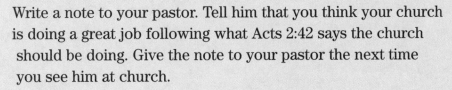

Thank God that you can be a part of what your church does to help others. Ask Him to help you understand that you are not too young to make a difference!

Earlier this week (Day Two), you wrote down three things that you were going to ask to help do at your church. Have you talked with anyone about those things?

Learn it!

Do you think sometimes that no one will listen to you because you are too young? Read 1 Timothy 4:12. What do you think Paul was telling Timothy in this verse? In your own words, write in the space below what Paul said to Timothy:

_____

_____

_____

_____

_____

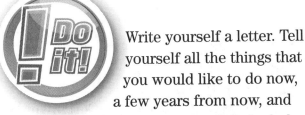 Write yourself a letter. Tell yourself all the things that you would like to do now, a few years from now, and when you are an adult. Include all the things you think God is telling you to do for Him. You can put this letter in your Memory Box. Make a list of things below that you want to include in your letter.

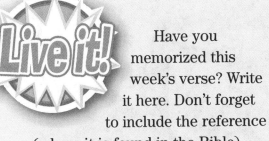 Have you memorized this week's verse? Write it here. Don't forget to include the reference (where it is found in the Bible) with your verse. It's important to memorize the reference each time you memorize a new Bible verse. If you can't remember the verse, try to memorize it today.

When you are finished writing your letter, seal it in an envelope. Write on the envelope today's date a year from now and put your name on it. If you already have a copy of a calendar for next year, write yourself a reminder to get your letter from your Memory Box.

When you read the letter next year, you can add to it anything that you think God is telling you to do or any changes you have made in things that you want to do. Then seal it in another envelope. Write on it: "Do not open until _____." Fill in a date five years from now.

The next time you are in church, say this week's memory verse to your teacher or friend. Then tell him why you want to come to church!

 Thank God for giving you gifts and abilities so that you can serve Him in your church.

Learn it!

Look up 1 Corinthians 12:12-27. This is a long passage in the Bible. Ask your mom, dad, or another adult to read this with you.

The "body" that this Scripture is talking about is a way of describing the church. Our churches function kind of like our bodies. No part of your body is more important than the other. That is why it takes everyone working together at church to be able to reach neighborhoods for Christ. No one person is more important than another person. This means that it takes everyone. That includes you!

Look at the outline of the body. What are some of the uses of different parts of the body? For example, what do the hands do? the nose? the eyes? In each box on the body outline, write something that particular part of the body does. What happens if one of these parts doesn't work? If the eyes do not work, does another part see?

Look at the body illustration again. Think about the way church members work together. Every person in the church family is different.

The hand could be the church members who prepare food for others. The feet could be the church members who go and visit people who are in the hospital. The feet could also be the people who go to tell others about Jesus (like your pastor or a missionary). Can you think of other examples? Write your ideas next to the body part on the illustration.

This activity is to help you understand 1 Corinthians 12:12-27 better. If you have questions, ask your parents or your teacher to help you understand. They'll be happy to help you with this assignment!

Make a list here of questions you want to ask.

_____
_____
_____
_____
_____
_____
_____

Thank God that He made people to need each other. Ask God to help you know how you can help others.

Find and read Psalm 100:4.

This verse is part of a song of praise to God. What is the name of your favorite song of praise to God?

Sing your song of praise as a prayer to God.

Week 3
Day SEVEN

Find and read Galatians 5:22-23.

As you grow as a Christian, God will help you grow in these ways. List the nine characteristics mentioned in this passage.

_____
_____
_____
_____

Think about it: How could these characteristics be helpful in your church?

35

Week 4
Day ONE

What is the greatest news you have ever heard? Did you keep the news to yourself or did you share it with someone else? Becoming a Christian is the greatest change that will ever take place in your life, and you need to tell others about it. You also need to tell other people how they can become Christians.

This week you will learn about how you can study your Bible to learn more about Jesus. When you study and learn more about Jesus, you will be able to tell other people about Him.

FIND IT!

Find Psalm 119:11 in your Bible. Print this verse on a 3-by-5-inch card and begin learning it. This is your memory verse for this week. David wrote these words many years ago. He knew the importance of learning the Word of God (the Bible) so that when he was tempted to sin, he would have verses to help him not to sin. Reading the Bible each day is important to help you know more about how to live as a Christian.

PRAY IT!

Thank God for the Bible. Ask Him to help you read and learn from it each day.

Learn it! The Bible is a special and unusual book. It is special because God told men what to write and how to write it. No other book in the whole world is like the Bible. More copies of the Bible have been sold than any other book in history! More people have read the Bible than any other book.

The Bible is a true book about men and women who learned to follow God. The people you read about in the Bible lived a long time ago. You can learn about God by reading about their lives and how they followed God.

When you read your Bible, you will discover things you do not understand. Keep a notebook nearby to list questions you have. Then you can ask your parents, your Sunday School teacher, or your pastor to help you find the answers. These people will be glad to help you find the answers about the Bible. They will be proud of you for studying your Bible. Do you have a question about something you have read in the Bible? If you do, write it here:

_____

_____

Do it! The Bible is divided into two parts. Look at the contents page in your Bible. What are the two parts?

_____ Testament and _____ Testament

Did you find the Old Testament and the New Testament? How many books are in the

Old Testament? _____

How many books are in the

New Testament? _____

Adding the two numbers you listed, how many total books are there in the Bible?

Old Testament Books _____

New Testament Books _____

Total Number of Books in the Bible _____

Check your answer by using your decoder and looking at the red circle at the top of page 36.

Then have fun learning the books of the New Testament by working the word search puzzle on page 46!

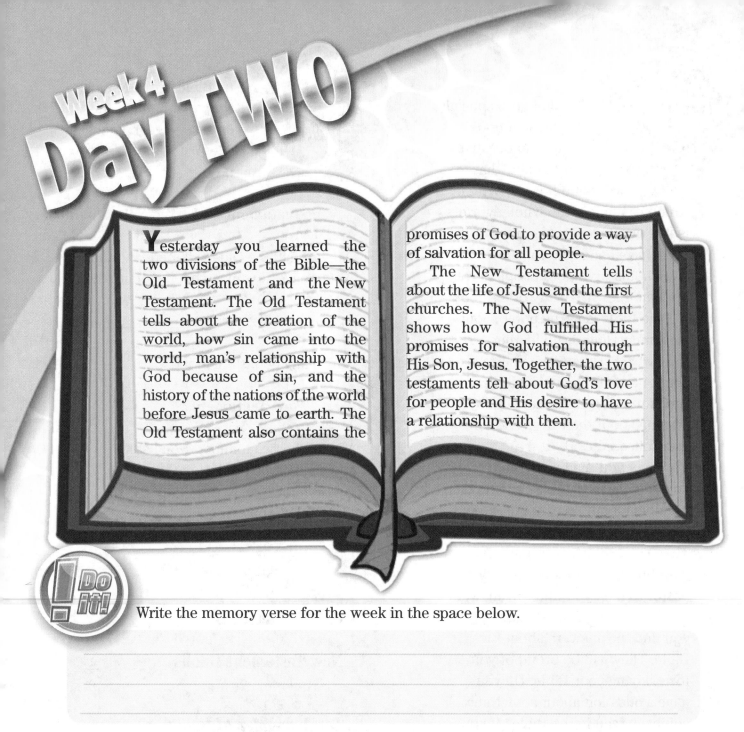

Yesterday you learned the two divisions of the Bible—the Old Testament and the New Testament. The Old Testament tells about the creation of the world, how sin came into the world, man's relationship with God because of sin, and the history of the nations of the world before Jesus came to earth. The Old Testament also contains the promises of God to provide a way of salvation for all people.

The New Testament tells about the life of Jesus and the first churches. The New Testament shows how God fulfilled His promises for salvation through His Son, Jesus. Together, the two testaments tell about God's love for people and His desire to have a relationship with them.

Do it! Write the memory verse for the week in the space below.

Use your pencil to circle words you do not understand in the memory verse. Find a dictionary to look up the words you do not understand and write a definition for each word. Then write the verse in your own words.

Some people memorize Bible verses, but they do not understand what the verses really mean. When you read a Bible verse that you do not understand, ask your parents or someone at your church to help you understand it. It will be easier to remember a verse if you understand what it means.

How Do I Study My Bible?

There are several ways to study your Bible. Here are three of them.

1. Study one book of the Bible. As you study one book, here are some questions to answer about that book:
   - Who wrote the book and when was it written?
   - What is the main point of this book?
   - What does this book say about God?
   - Who are people and where are places discussed in this book?
   - What is God teaching me through this book?

2. Study one person in the Bible. You may need a special book to help you study about a person. A concordance is a book that lists Bible references that use a particular word in a passage. You could use a concordance to look up a person's name and make a list of Bible passages where that name is listed. Here are some questions to answer about studying a person in the Bible:
   - Where did this person live?
   - What events took place in this person's life?
   - What important decisions did this person make?
   - How did the decisions this person made affect him or her?
   - What can I learn from this person?
   - What is God teaching me through this person's life?

3. Study one specific verse. Gather several different translations of the Bible. As you read the verse in other translations, answer the following questions. When you have answered the questions, write the verse in your own words. Memorize the verse you have studied.
   - What are the important words in the verse?
   - What are the definitions of those words?
   - What is God teaching me through this verse?

The Holman Bible Concordance for Kids is designed to help you learn more about the Bible. If you do not have a copy, ask your parents or your Sunday School teacher to help you get a copy. The book can be ordered from the LifeWay Christian Resources Web site, *www.lifeway.com,* or by calling toll-free 1-800-458-2772.

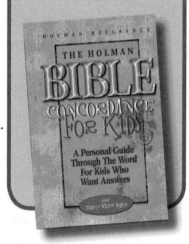

Ask God to help you understand the Bible verses you are learning and how the verses can help you in your life.

39

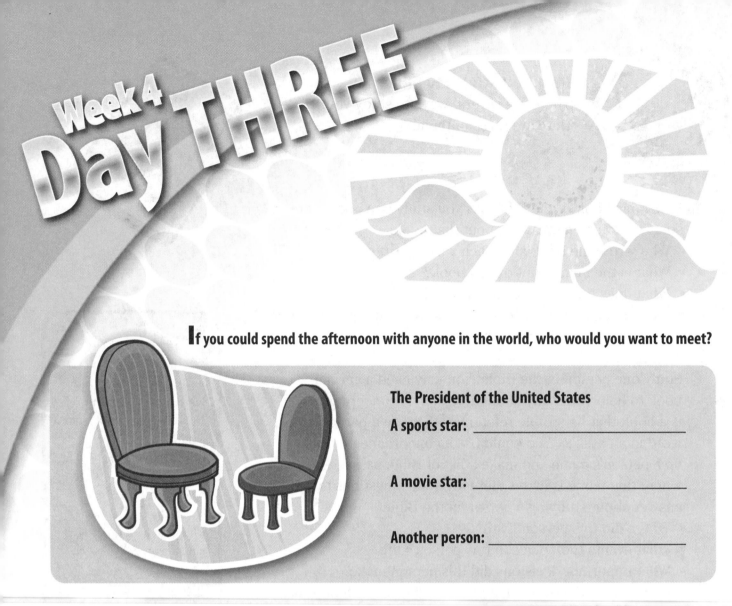

If you could spend the afternoon with anyone in the world, who would you want to meet?

The President of the United States

A sports star: _____

A movie star: _____

Another person: _____

If you could spend only one afternoon with this person, how much about the person would you get to know? You probably would not discover very much about the person in a short amount of time. To learn about someone, you have to spend a lot of time with her and talk to her.

Learn it! Although God already knows everything about you, there are lots of things you do not know about God. You can learn about God when you spend time with Him. God wants you to talk with Him and tell Him what you are thinking, how you are feeling, what your dreams are, and what your needs are. Spending time with God means spending time reading your Bible and praying.

 **PRAY it!** Read through the four parts of prayer described on page 41. Think about each part. Read the prayer that you wrote while working through the ACTS activity. Thank God for always hearing your prayers.

Open your Bible to 1 Thessalonians 5:17 and read the verse. When does the verse say you should pray?

—

What do you think *prayer* means?

_____

_____

_____

Prayer is talking and listening to God. When you pray, take time to listen. Listening to God is an important part of prayer. You can listen to God as you read the Bible and pay attention to what it says. You can listen to God by paying attention to thoughts that you have about doing what it right. When you pray, talk to God like you would talk to a good friend. You do not have to use special words to talk with God. He knows what you are trying to say.

The best advice taught about prayer is in the Book of Matthew. Open your Bible to Matthew 6:5-13 and read the passage. Jesus taught that your prayers need to be private and personal. When you pray, you do not need to use big words in order to impress others who might hear you. Use words that you would use every day.

When you pray, think about the following parts of prayer. The highlighted letters spell ACTS. When you pray, ACTS might help you. In the space after each statement, write a short sentence for a prayer according to that description. When you finish, you will have written a short prayer!

A **doration** is praising God for who He is and what He has done.

C **onfession** is admitting to God what you have done wrong (confessing your sin) and asking Him to forgive you.

T **hanksgiving** is telling God how thankful you are for the things He has given you.

S **upplication** is asking God for the things you need and praying for others.

As you pray through the parts of prayer listed above, remember that God always hears your prayers. Also remember that He may not always answer your prayers the way you want. You must trust that God knows what is best for you.

Week 4 Day FOUR

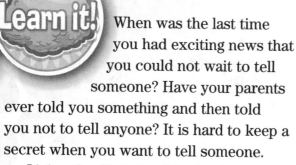

When was the last time you had exciting news that you could not wait to tell someone? Have your parents ever told you something and then told you not to tell anyone? It is hard to keep a secret when you want to tell someone.

Living the Christian life should not be a secret. Since you have become a Christian, you should tell others about Jesus. Your testimony is important. You read about what a testimony is during the first week.

What is a testimony? Write your answer below. (If you need help, go back to Day Five of the first week on page 12.)

Read Psalm 66:16. What does this verse tell you to do?

_____

_____

How can you do what Psalm 66:16 tells you to do?

_____

Who is the first person you want to tell?

_____

Thank God for the difference He has made in your life.

Live it!

In the space below, write your testimony just as if you were telling it to your best friend. When you have finished, go back to the questions you answered during the first week (page 12) and see if you included everything. When you tell someone about Jesus, include the answers to those questions without sounding like you are answering questions. It may seem hard at first. Keep working on it. The more you tell others your testimony, the easier it will become!

_____'s Testimony

(write your name here)

Review it!

The last four weeks have been important in your life. You have learned about how to become a Christian, what baptism and the Lord's Supper are, what the church is, how to study your Bible and pray, and how to share your testimony. Let's see how much you can remember!

Ask your parents or another adult to listen to you as you share the following Bible verses and tell what they mean. Can you share these verses without looking at the Bible or the cards you made each week?

Psalm 119:11

Psalm 122:1

John 3:16

John 15:14

You have also learned some new words this past month. Can you match the meaning of the words to their correct definitions on page 45?

To discover if your answers are correct, use your decoder to check the correct answers inside the red oval.

____ 1. Christian   A. to turn from disobeying God to obeying Him

____ 2. Save   B. actions, attitudes, words, or thoughts that do not please God

____ 3. Sin   C. talking to God and listening to Him

____ 4. Lord's Supper   D. telling about your experience

____ 5. Baptism   E. a special time to help Christians remember Jesus' death

____ 6. Repent   F. the name given to a person who has asked Jesus to be his Lord and Savior

____ 7. Testimony   G. to be rescued, brought to safety, or delivered from the judgment of sin

____ 8. Prayer   H. obeying God by being put under water to show that you have become a Christian

Week 4 Day SIX

Find and read Colossians 3:17.

What does this verse mean to you?

Ask God to help you do what this verse says to do.

Week 4 Day SEVEN

Find and read 1 Timothy 4:12.

How can you be an example to others?

Ask God to help you be a good example to others.

New Testament Book Search

Use your Bible to find the books of the New Testament in the puzzle below. (Book names with a number in front of the names are only listed one time; for example, 1 Corinthians is listed as *Corinthians*; *John* is listed two times.)

```
S M L U E K U L U V D S X B W Q
N N P T H E S S A L O N I A N S
Y A A W E H T T A M S A C L S H
F H W I R E V E L A T I O N N K
G Q T D H S N I J P Z P S P A P
S A J O N T U H H O S P W E I E
T I L A M J N I O N Z I E T S O
C G M A M I L I A J E L R E E U
A O R M T E T I R D H I B R H A
R K L I M I S A U O N H E G P C
R D G O D S A J Z H C P H N E D
N B N D O A X N T I T U S X M L
X H I L M E Q S I W B B V C M
L B O O S K C B Q H J J M D U C
O C X J X Z M V X Y Y H T L R D
```

Use your decoder to check your answers.

All About Me

Complete the All About Me box and put it in your Memory Box.
If you have not been baptized, add that date later.

Today's date _____

I am _____ years old.

My best friend is _____.

My pastor's name is _____.

_____ is my teacher at church.

People who help me know about Jesus are _____

_____

_____

_____.

Other kids in my class at church are_____

_____

_____ .

I became a Christian on _____ .
                            (fill in date)

I was baptized on _____ .
                       (fill in date)